T3-BWP-494

River Grove Cleanup

SRA

Columbus, OH

SRAonline.com

 SRA

Copyright © 2008 by SRA/McGraw-Hill.

All rights reserved. No part of this publication may be reproduced or distributed in any form or by any means, or stored in a database or retrieval system, without the prior written consent of The McGraw-Hill Companies, Inc., including, but not limited to, network storage or transmission, or broadcast for distance learning.
An Open Court Curriculum.

Printed in China.

Send all inquiries to this address:
SRA/McGraw-Hill
4400 Easton Commons
Columbus, OH 43219

ISBN: 978-0-07-608513-2
MHID: 0-07-608513-9

3 4 5 6 7 8 9 NOR 13 12 11

The McGraw-Hill Companies

Maya and Ana were playing tag. The fence
was the base. Ana tagged Maya, but Maya was
already touching the fence.

"I'm safe!" giggled Maya. The girls leaned on the fence to catch their breath. Ana looked around the playground.

"Look at that litter!" she said. She sounded furious.

4

On warm days kids ate lunch on the picnic tables. Some of the students of River Grove School were litterbugs!

"We should all clean up our school," said Maya sadly. "Let's have a class cleanup day!"

"That's a good idea!" agreed Ana. "Let's tell Miss Johns!" The girls raced toward Miss Johns.

Miss Johns was the gym teacher. She was strict sometimes, but everyone liked her.

"Fabulous idea, girls," said Miss Johns. "Let's go inside and tell the class."

The class agreed that there was a litter problem. They picked Wednesday for the cleanup day.

On Wednesday the children were eager to get moving. "Listen here!" yelled Miss Johns. "Make a line. We will form a giant human comb and pick up all the trash."

8

"Are you ready?" asked Miss Johns.

"Yes!" responded the children.

"Start your engines!"

The children made motor sounds: "Vroom!
Vroom!"

"GO!" shouted Miss Johns. In a flash, the children covered the playground like an army of ants. They picked up sandwich bags and juice boxes. They yanked empty cans from bushes. They filled bag after bag.

Soon the children reached the other side of the playground. They all smiled.

"Look at that!" Miss Johns applauded. "The playground sparkles and glows! Now go out and enjoy it!"

Vocabulary

litter (lit´ ər) (page 4) *n.* Scattered paper and other materials; trash.

furious (fyûr´ ē əs) (page 4) *adj.* Very angry.

engines (en´ jinz) (page 9) *n.* Plural form of **engine:** A machine that uses energy to run other machines.

flash (flash) (page 10) *n.* An instant.

yanked (yangkt) (page 10) *v.* Past tense of **yank:** To pull.

glows (glōz) (page 11) *v.* Shines.

Comprehension Focus: Making Inferences

1. Page 4 says that Ana was furious. Why was she upset?

2. How do you think the children will treat the playground after their cleanup day?

W8-BTM-150

W9-BTW-420